CONTENTS

good spelling

Pedigree®

Published 2011.
Pedigree Books Ltd, Beech Hill House,
Walnut Gardens, Exeter, Devon EX4 4DH
books@pedigreegroup.co.uk
www.pedigreebooks.com

POKÉMON™

£7.99

Step Into UNOVA

From the first fated moment when Ash stepped into the Unova region, the Trainer knew that this was a region he had to explore! The skyline of Unova is peppered with dramatic cityscapes, towering skyscrapers and untold natural wonders. This intriguing mix of urban bustle and remote wilderness is a wonder to behold.

Fascinating new Pokémon dwell at every twist and turn in Unova, each with their own unique powers and Abilities. Although many species live side-by-side with the region's human inhabitants, there are others that are so elusive they have rarely been sighted. Among the most famous of these are the Legendary Pokémon Reshiram and Zekrom. These titans have dominated myths and folklore in Unova for generations!

There is much for new Trainers to learn about the region – adventure and excitement waits at every turn! Read this beginner's guide to Unova's key locations and then scour the pages of this Annual for vital facts and stats about the Pokémon that live here. Good luck!

◢ NUVEMA TOWN

This is location number one for new Trainers! They come here to visit Professor Juniper's research lab and take on the Pokémon that will join them in their battles throughout the region.

First Pokémon

In Unova, each Trainer can choose one of three species as their first Pokémon – Snivy, Tepig or Oshawott.

◢ STRIATON CITY

This beautiful city lies in the southeast of Unova. The city's Gym is also a restaurant with three Gym Leaders called Cilan, Chili and Cress. The Gym holds a special meaning for Ash because he held his first Unova Gym battle here.

◢ PINWHEEL FOREST

It is easy to get lost in this vast area of woodland, vines and vegetation! Mossy glades mingle with crystal waterfalls and caves, all beneath a thick canopy of green. Ash catches his Sewaddle in Pinwheel Forest.

◢ NACRENE CITY

This stylish metropolitan centre is known as the City of Art, since it has many warehouses that have been turned into galleries. The Nacrene Gym is also a museum and the Gym Leader, Lenora, specialises in Normal-type Pokémon.

ASH IS BACK!

After their adventures in the Sinnoh region, Ash Ketchum and his best friend Pikachu are determined to sample everything that Unova has to offer!

The pals first discovered the region when they and Ash's mum tagged along on a trip with Professor Oak. The young Trainer was knocked out by the new species of Pokémon that he met, setting off on a quest to beat Unova's Gyms and become the best Trainer in the land.

▲ASH

Ash has caught a bunch of new species already, but Pikachu will always be his right hand Pokémon. Although the friends got off to a shaky start, they've been loyal to each other ever since they first left Ash's home in Pallet Town. Along the way, they've got through countless battles, scrapes and scary situations. Both Ash and Pikachu know that when the chips are down, they can rely on each other to save the day.

TAKE A LOOK AT ASH'S ALL NEW PACK OF POKÉMON!

TEPIG
Abandoned by its first Trainer, Ash rescued Tepig when it was a hungry stray.

OSHAWOTT
This Pokémon ran off from Professor Juniper's lab on its quest to follow Ash.

SNIVY
Snivy is a Pokémon that uses Attract to befuddle its opponents.

PIDOVE
A Normal and Flying-type that Ash catches to add to the team.

SCRAGGY
A stubborn Pokémon that hatches out of an Egg during Ash's early days in Unova.

SEWADDLE
A Pokémon that uses the sensory bumps on its forehead to touch and greet other beings.

New Friends ON THE BLOCK

Although Team Rocket is bound to appear to mess things up, Ash and Pikachu won't be alone in Unova. Their new friends Iris and Cilan are there to show them around and watch their backs every step of the way!

As the group journey through Unova's cities and countryside, Ash finds himself seeking Iris and Cilan's help many times a day. The friends are always ready to introduce the Trainer to new Pokémon species and fill him in on the rivals and Gym Leaders operating in the region.

◢ IRIS

Is only a young girl, but she has the pluck and determination to hold her own in any situation. She and Ash get off to a prickly start, but the pair soon learn to rub along together without too many arguments! Iris is high-spirited, outspoken and bold, but she's also an outdoor girl who's totally at home in nature.

AXEW
This Dragon-type is Iris' Pokémon partner. It has been noted to travel in her hair rather than a Poké Ball.

◢CILAN

Cilan met Ash and his pals when he was out shopping in Striaton City. He and his brothers Chili and Cress are all Gym Leaders. Ash has done well in choosing Cilan as a friend – his new buddy is knowledgeable, patient and kind. Cilan uses his vast experience as a Pokémon connoisseur to size up the compatibility between Trainers and their Pokémon, offering tips as to how they might best get along. He is also a wonderful cook.

PANSAGE

Cilan travels with his Grass-type Pansage. It is a good-natured and cheerful companion.

Rocket Roll-out

Wherever Ash and Pikachu roam, Team Rocket are never too far behind! This time the criminal outfit have raised their game, obsessed with wreaking havoc on a global scale. The terrible trio of Jessie, James and Meowth have made a villainous vow to rock Unova from top to bottom, intent on taking the region over for their own nasty ends.

Ash has got to stay alert, Team Rocket are going to be tracking every move he makes. The threesome are always waiting for the right moment to swoop in and steal Pikachu. No trick is too low, no plan too sneaky, whether it's underhand disguises, con tricks or double-dealing.

Luckily Team Rocket's brains aren't as big as their boasts! Jessie, James and Meowth's plans are over-ambitious to the extreme. So far Ash has easily outsmarted his enemies. Let's hope his luck continues in Unova...

◢ JESSIE

The self-appointed leader of the group is short-tempered and vain. She's got far too much attitude to admit that she needs James and Meowth, but inside she knows they're the only friends that she's got.

WOOBAT

This was the first Pokémon Jessie captured in Unova. It is a Psychic- and Flying-type with a distinctive heart-shaped nostril.

JAMES

James surprised everyone by turning his back on his wealthy family in order to join Team Rocket's band of renegades. Although he is a hardened criminal, he has a very soft spot for each of his Pokémon.

MEOWTH

Although he is a Normal-type Pokémon, Team Rocket's Meowth is one of a kind. Since teaching himself to speak like a human, he's found the gift of the gab! Meowth can't help hatching crazy plans at any opportunity.

PIKACHU PROBLEM

Ash's beloved Pikachu has got lost in this sparky crowd of Pokémon – can you help the Trainer get him back? Only one of the Pikachu on this page exactly matches this photo of Ash's best pal. Draw a circle around the correct one.

A B C D

E F G H

I J K L

Did you know? Pikachu are native to the Kanto region, although they have been spotted in other regions too. In the wild they dwell in forests, often living in large groups.

TEN IN TEN?

Getting your bearings amongst Unova's network of bridges, forests and cities takes time. Gym Leader Cilan has put the pressure on by challenging you to find ten top Unova region locations in ten minutes! Start by searching for Cilan's beautiful hometown of Striaton, then scour the grid until you've crossed off every one.

D	Y	T	I	C	N	O	T	A	I	R	T	S	R	W
Y	F	J	K	D	U	N	D	E	L	L	A	B	A	Y
N	T	S	E	R	O	F	L	E	E	H	W	N	I	P
W	B	I	C	H	F	H	G	H	E	R	W	U	N	U
O	P	Z	C	D	S	C	X	I	T	O	C	U	B	K
T	J	H	T	E	K	M	J	S	T	B	Q	E	O	L
A	M	K	J	K	N	N	S	A	B	U	K	M	W	S
I	J	G	N	G	B	E	L	F	H	S	P	A	U	Z
R	M	Q	A	B	Z	U	R	X	D	C	T	T	A	W
U	X	C	S	D	M	M	C	C	W	B	S	O	L	R
X	S	H	Z	U	S	Y	X	G	A	J	X	W	L	F
U	F	G	C	H	C	T	W	R	B	N	Y	N	E	T
L	D	C	T	T	F	G	H	I	G	T	T	G	Y	J
C	A	S	T	E	L	I	A	C	I	T	Y	B	N	L
K	E	G	D	I	R	B	W	O	R	R	A	Y	K	S

Remember! The Unova locations could be hiding anywhere in this letter square. Words could be running vertically, horizontally, diagonally or even in reverse!

STRIATON CITY ✓   NACRENE CITY ✓   RAINBOW VALLEY ✓

NUVEMA TOWN ✓   LUXURIA TOWN ✓   ACCUMULA TOWN ✓

PINWHEEL FOREST ✓   SKYARROW BRIDGE ✓   UNDELLA BAY ✓

CASTELIA CITY ✓

TYPE TEST

Do you have a natural eye for Pokémon types? There are 17 types – every species that you encounter will belong to one or even two of these. This quick quiz will help you assess your recognition skills. Just draw a line to match the Pokémon with the correct type – can you suss out all eight?

1 MUNNA

2 GALVANTULA

3 PATRAT

4 SCRAGGY

5 DRILBUR

6 AXEW

7 DARUMAKA

8 SWANNA

A Fire

B Normal

C Psychic

D Water/Flying

E Bug/Electric

F Dragon

G Dark/Fighting

H Ground

Make your SELECTION

In the Unova region, Professor Juniper is responsible for giving Trainers their Pokémon. Each new Trainer can choose either Snivy, Tepig or Oshawott. Which would suit you best? Select your ideal first Pokémon, then colour it in using bright crayons or felt-tips. In the space beside, write a sentence explaining your choice.

SNIVY

I'd like to travel with Snivy because... he cook more sensive and more attck
oliver
oliver

TEPIG

I'd like to travel with Tepig because... he is cute when he is coloured in and with out couler
Jake because I think he has good power

OSHAWOTT

I'd like to travel with Oshawott because...
could spray water
absome one
they amazeouise

A SANDILE GUSHER OF CHANGE!

Ash has started his quest for Unova region Pokémon, his heart still set on becoming a Pokémon Master. The Trainer is heading for his first Unova region Gym challenge in Striaton City, accompanied by a young girl called Iris...

Ash looked over his shoulder. Whichever path he took, Iris was there, tailing behind him. He tried walking faster, but the girl just picked up the pace!

"Why are you coming along with me anyway?" he demanded.

"Excuse me," sniffed Iris. "It's not that I'm coming along with you, it's that you're coming along with me!"

Iris elbowed her way in front, shoving Ash and Pikachu to the side of the path.

"Puh-leze!" yelled the Trainer, barging his way ahead again.

"I figured that since you don't know the Unova region, I'd help you out," replied Iris. "But I don't even get a thank you!"

Ash glared at her. He didn't remember asking this girl to tag along on his journey and he certainly didn't plan on thanking her!

In no time the hot-headed pair were stood with their hands on their hips, shouting at maximum volume. It took the arrival of a little Pokémon to stun them into silence!

"It's an Oshawott," cried Iris.

Ash gasped. He'd seen this Pokémon before! A plucky little Oshawott had helped the Trainer see off an attack from Team Rocket just a few days' earlier. It had to be the same one! He flicked open his Pokédex.

"Thanks for helping us out back there," said Ash. "Were you following us?"

The Oshawott beamed up at the Trainer, scuttling over to grab his trouser legs.

OSHAWOTT

THE SEA OTTER POKÉ

Oshawott attacks and defends using the scalchop that c... be removed from stomach.

Iris rushed over to Oshawott, scooping it into her arms.

"You are so cute," she gushed. "And you were following me! Since it's obvious that you can't live without me, I'll promise that I'll keep you as my very own Pokémon."

Iris hugged the poor Oshawott so hard, Ash thought it was going to suffocate!

The Pokémon shook its head, clambering to get free. Iris's jaw dropped as the Oshawott leapt onto Ash's shoulder.

Oshawott nudged its way into the Trainer's neck, shoving Pikachu to the ground!

"What's going on?" yelled Ash.

"Are you saying that you like Ash?" asked Iris.

Oshawott bounced up and down. Pikachu dusted itself off then tried to blast the intruder with a bolt of electricity, but somehow its rival deflected it back onto Ash.

The hapless Trainer was sent crashing to the ground, much to Iris and Axew's enjoyment.

Iris giggled. Although it had knocked him over, she was starting to get the feeling that Oshawott wanted to be caught by Ash!

"Whatddya know?" grinned Ash. "Well since you helped us out with Team Rocket, why don't you come along with us?"

Oshawott's face filled with pleasure, but when Ash tried to capture it in his Poké Ball, the Poké Ball simply bounced off the Pokémon's head!

"Why did that happen?" wondered the Trainer.

Suddenly he remembered – this had to be the Oshawott from Professor Juniper's lab!

"I guess that would mean that Oshawott's Poké Ball is at the Professor's lab too," he decided. "Come on!"

Ash and Iris stopped in at a local store to videolink Professor Juniper.

"So that's where Oshawott went," smiled the professor. "I was so worried. It left without letting me know."

Ash grinned at the monitor. Oshawott must have been keen to catch up with him!

"If it wouldn't be too much bother," continued the professor, "maybe you could take care of Oshawott from now on?"

Ash was totally psyched! Within moments the Poké Ball was transferred over to him. The Trainer scooped it up, ready to take on his new charge.

Professor Juniper gave one word of warning before she signed off.

"Since Oshawott has a tendency to disappear," she reminded him. "Keep an eye out for it!"

Ash waved goodbye, then glanced around the store. True to form, Oshawott was out of sight!

The kids ran outside, but the Pokémon had disappeared.

"This is nuts!" yelled Ash. "Where would Oshawott go?"

"I guess I'll just have to help you look around," announced smiling at her Axew.

"I can do it myself, thank Ash blurted out.

She didn't care in the slig that she might be driving he friend crazy.

"Since we're both Pokém Trainers, you don't have to around acting like a little k know," Iris replied.

"Let's go, Pikachu," sni walking away.

Iris ran after the pair, b the ground suddenly gave Ash, you and their Pokémon all fou themselves tumbling into giant hole!

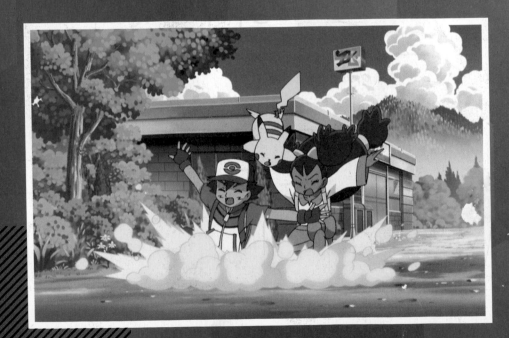

"That hurt!" groaned Ash, rubbing his shoulder.

Iris pulled herself out of the dirt. The muddy hole was so deep, they'd never be able to climb out of it.

"What's going on?" she wondered. "It looks like a trap."

Ash checked that Pikachu was OK, then tried to peer out of the hole. All he could see was sky. Something didn't add up – the ground shouldn't just open up like that!

"If it is a trap, who could have done this?" he asked.

Suddenly a boy's face leant over the edge of the hole. He could answer Ash's question in a single word.

"Sandile."

Not far away, Team Rocket were travelling undercover. They were on an urgent mission to capture Pikachu and then report to their boss!

"We may have fallen short last time," admitted James. "But we'll get him this time!"

Meowth smirked. "Success is as sure as the day is long!"

It only took one more step for their first hitch to present itself – the threesome suddenly found themselves plunging into a crater-sized hole!

"It looks like somebody else has been busy digging pit traps!" screeched Jessie. "But the question is who?"

"Sandile," said a Pokémon voice.

The trio of crooks leapt in surprise. There, on the other side of the hole was a Pokémon wearing a pair of red sunglasses!

"What have we here?" gasped James. "It's an unfamiliar Pokémon."

While Team Rocket were making the Sandile's acquaintance, the boy pulled Ash and Iris out of their hole.

As soon as they got back on safe ground, Ash read up on the Sandile Pokémon.

SANDILE
THE DESERT CROC POKÉMON
A dark membrane protects its eyes from the sun and it buries itself in the sand with its eyes and nose sticking out.

"I can't thank you enough for helping us," said Iris.

The boy smiled. "My name is Dan. My family operates a resort spa hotel that's not far from here!"

Iris grabbed his hands in delight. She loved resort spa hotels!

"Our hot sand spa is our hotel's biggest attraction," explained Dan. "But I'm sorry to say that we're closed right now because of Sandile."

Dan led Ash and Iris up to his family's hotel. The place looked beautiful, but it was completely deserted. All the hot sand beds lay empty, pitted with Sandile holes.

"It happened just a short time ago," sighed Dan.

He explained how he and his Dad used to welcome lots of guests who loved taking relaxing sand baths! Wild Sandile would show up too, but they never hurt anyone, he said.

Ash and Iris listened intently as Dan explained that one day the Sandile starting blasting holes all over the resort! The guests were driven out and for now at least, it didn't look as though they were coming back.

"I don't understand how a bunch of friendly Sandile could have suddenly gotten destructive," frowned Iris.

"Neither do we," sighed Dan.

Ash and Pikachu knew what they had to do – it was time to get to the bottom of the Sandile mystery!

"Where are we going to start?" asked Iris.

"Before we figure it out, we need to do some research!" grinned Ash. "This is the best!"

Iris huffed with irritation as the Trainer pulled on some board shorts and joined Pikachu in the sand baths. She was about to give him another telling-off, when Axew jumped down and took its place next to Pikachu!

While Pikachu and his pals relaxed, Team Rocket had scrambled free and made their own way to Dan's hotel. Jessie, James and Meowth were crouched behind some lumber, planning their attack.

"It appears that the twerp is having the time of his life," sniggered James.

"Which gives us the perfect chance!" agreed Jessie.

"Sandile!"

The Desert Croc Pokémon with the red sunglasses burst out of the sand behind them. It seemed to be determined to blow the villains' cover!

"I think it's time that you became scarce," hissed Meowth.

The sand baths were good – so good, that Ash almost forgot he was meant to be helping Dan! He was dusting the sand off his shorts when he spotted someone else enjoying the spa's facilities.

Oshawott! The little Pokémon was stretched out in the sunshine, its head resting on a neatly folded towel.

"Have you been lying here all this time?" marvelled Ash. "That's one happy Pokémon!"

Unfortunately there was no time to celebrate Oshawott's return. The friends turned round to discover the Sandile leader in the red sunglasses was channeling towards them through the ground. The Pokémon burst out of the sand, snatching Iris's Axew in its mighty jaws!

"We'll save you!" roared Ash. "Pikachu! Thunderbolt, let's go!"

Iris threw herself across the Trainer's path.

"If you use Thunderbolt then Axew will get hurt!" she wailed.

Instead, the plucky girl dropped to her knees and began tugging at Sandile. Ash and Pikachu joined in, pulling with all their strength.

It was a doomed struggle. Now that Sandile's jaws had locked on, nothing was going to loosen its grip.

Iris was giving up hope when Pikachu's ear accidentally tickled Sandile's nose. The Pokémon released Axew in a noisy sneeze, but then caught Pikachu and Oshawott in its mouth.

"No!" cried Ash, as the Sandile leader scuttled towards the undergrowth behind the spa.

Before Sandile could get very far, Team Rocket appeared on the horizon driving a stolen crane! Ash watched in dismay as the huge machine dropped its magnetic gripper, lifting Sandile, Pikachu and Oshawott high into the air.

"We bring the white light of evil into your future!" sneered Jessie.

"Hammering justice onto the black universe," added James.

Meowth rounded off the war cry. "Carving our names in the rock of eternity!"

"Give us back our Pokémon!" bellowed Ash, running after the giant crane.

"There's a huge flaw in your premise," retorted Jessie. "They're our Pokémon now!"

Meowth rubbed his paws together, eyeing up their catch. Oshawott and Sandile made the perfect bonus prize! The over-excited crooks began to drive the crane up the mountainside.

"Let's inform the Boss right away!" chuckled James.

Ash, Iris and Dan charged after the crane, clambering over rocks in their bid to catch-up with the lumbering machine. Jessie cackled with delight to see her enemy struggle. Just then a deep rumble echoed around the mountainside.

"What's happening?" she gasped, as dozens of Sandile burst out of the ground around them.

"Stay away from us!" yelped Meowth. "All of you!"

The Sandile weren't listening. They were getting closer and closer. Droves of formidable Pokémon closed in on the crane, rocking the earth beneath its tyres.

"Let's get out of here James!" ordered Jessie. "Right away!"

Too late. With a terrific rumble, the ground beneath the crane collapsed! The machine disappeared into a huge hole, releasing its grip on Pikachu, Oshawott and the Sandile leader.

The Pokémon crawled to safety, leaving Team Rocket to blast their way out of the pit.

"Team," groaned James. "We've got no choice but to retreat."

Ash, Iris and Dan watched as the Sandile leader gently dropped Pikachu and Oshawott in front of a herd of wild Pokémon. Frightened Deerling, Patrat and Pidove were all huddled together on the mountainside.

Suddenly a jet of water burst out of the ground. The Sandile with the sunglasses started to guide the wild Pokémon away from the gushing torrent.

"That's a geyser!" shouted Dan. "I've never seen one around here. Geyser water is boiling hot!"

Ash looked across at the Sandile. More and more geysers were shooting up all around them.

"I bet you that the Sandile are trying to protect the other Pokémon," he said. "Those Sandile are alright!"

"I'm beginning to wonder if that's the reason that they came to the sand baths in the first place," nodded Dan. "They were trying to warn us about the geysers!"

Iris looked wide-eyed. "That must be why Sandile grabbed Axew!"

The gang moved in closer.

"Hey Pikachu!" bellowed Ash.
Pikachu and Oshawott scampered over to the Trainer, hoping their ordeal was over.

Ash had his Pokémon back, but geysers were erupting all over the mountainside. The ground started to rumble and shake. A thunderous series of geysers began to burst out of every crevice, dislodging the rocks.

"Oh no!" cried Iris, as a torrent of water split the mountainside in two. Boiling water was gushing from all directions.

The wild Pokémon stepped backwards, gripped in panic. The spit of solid ground that they were standing on broke away from the mountain, leaving them exposed on all sides.

"They're surrounded by boiling water!" gasped Iris. "What do we do?"

Dan shook his head.

"There's going to be trouble if another one blows," he frowned.

Another deafening crack rocked the mountainside.

"Like right now!" screamed Iris.

Ash ran towards the water – he had to do something to save the Pokémon!

"You can't wade through boiling water!" shouted Iris.

Just when it looked like they were out of options, the Sandile came forward.

"Look!" yelled Ash. "They're making a bridge!" The Sandile began to climb on each other's backs, using their powerful jaws to grab onto their tails. When the tower was as wide as the water, the Sandile gently swung over to the island. The Pokémon's escape route was set!

At first the wild Pokémon were too scared to use the Sandile bridge, but Ash ran over it to show that it was strong enough.

"We've got to hurry," he explained. "Let's cross this bridge together."

The wild Pokémon gingerly started to make their way over the bridge. Water bubbled and raged around the island, breaking off chunks of rock at alarming speed.

"There's not much time!" shouted Ash, catching the last Sandile in the chain before it could touch the smoking-hot water.

At that instant, another geyser erupted creating a boiling fountain above Ash's head. All the Pokémon were across now, but who was going to save the Trainer?

"Oshawott!"

Ash's newest Pokémon used a stunning Water Gun move to deflect the jet of water. The move worked brilliantly, but Oshawott began to tumble towards the rapids too!
Quick-thinking from Ash returned it to its Poké Ball in the nick of time.

Now Ash was on his own... until Iris grabbed his hand. The plucky girl had risked her own safety to climb over the Sandile bridge and pull Ash out. It was a massive effort – between them and the

Sandile and everyone had escaped unhurt!

"This is wonderful," said Iris a little later, relaxing at Dan's hotel spa. The geysers had wiped out the sands, but now the family could offer guests a new hot springs experience!

"This hot water feels awesome!" grinned Ash. "Five stars without a doubt."

"Thanks," said Dan. "We now have a brand new attraction!"

A perilous adventure for our heroes winds down with a little rest and relaxation before their Unova journey continues... on page 48!

CHANGING FACES

As he roams ever deeper into Unova, Ash is gradually learning about the Evolutions of the Pokémon species that are native to the region. The shadows of ten evolved forms are shown on the opposite page, can you name every one?

Study each Pokémon family, then write the correct Evolution solution into the crossword grid. If you get stuck, visit the Clue Centre on the facing page – the facts should help trigger a memory about the Pokémon you're searching for!

1 Pignite
2 Darmanitan
3 swadloon
4 zoroArk
1 tRanquiLL
2 Musharna
3 serviNE
4 Watchog
5 dewott

ACROSS

DOWN

CLUE CENTRE

Across

1. Belly fire intensifies when it gets angry.
2. Can wreck a dump truck with a single punch.
3. Wraps itself in leaves.
4. Has a dark red mane.

Down

1. Can find its way home from any location.
2. Pink mist flows from its forehead.
3. Expert at the Vine Whip move.
4. Raises its tail when enemies are sighted.
5. Powerful Water-type.
6. Drill made of steel.

ZANY ZOOMS

This page is crammed with crazy close-ups of your favourite Pokémon characters! Take a look at each photo and then write the correct names underneath.

1. RIIS
Iris

2. SAJEM
James

3. HAS
ash

4. NICAL
cilan

5. SESIJE
Jessie

6. PSOFRSORE NIPUJER
professor
Juniper

Need to find a new perspective? Use the anagram clues to help you.

THE ROAD TO STRIATON CITY

Ash and his feisty new friend Iris are on their way to Striaton City and Ash's first Unova Gym battle! Can you help the pals find their way? Trace a route through the Unova wilderness, avoiding blind alleys, boulders and trees. You should only travel up the same path twice.

START

STRIATON CITY

FINISH

MAKE YOUR OWN POKÉ BALL!

The Poké Ball is an essential device for every Trainer who wants to catch wild Pokémon. Now's your chance to make your own! Your homemade Poké Ball will look awesome displayed on a bedroom shelf or hung from your favourite rucksack.

You will need:
- Balloon
- PVA glue
- Scissors
- Paint brushes
- Old newspapers
- Strips of white kitchen towel
- Poster paint

1. Blow the balloon up to a size that fits comfortably in your hand. Tie a knot in the end.

2. Cover a worktop with old newspapers, then find a dish and mix up a few spoonfuls of PVA glue with an equal amount of water.

3. Dip a strip of kitchen towel into the glue paste, then drape it over the balloon. Repeat this until the whole balloon is covered, only leaving the knotted end free.

4. Keep pasting on kitchen towel strips until the balloon is coated in at least three layers.

5. Leave the balloon to dry for 24 hours. When it is ready, the kitchen towel will have formed a papier maché shell.

6. When the papier maché is completely dry, use scissors to carefully burst the balloon inside. Pull the rubber out and throw it away.

7. Pick the type of Poké Ball that you'd like to make. Most Trainers use the basic Poké Ball, but there are many more that you can choose from. Now it's time to use poster paints to carefully match the design. To get the Poké Ball just right, you may need to paint the colours in stages, allowing the shell to dry off in between each coat.

8. When your Poké Ball has been painted, it needs some shine! Mix up another batch of PVA glue and water, then brush the solution all over. Leave it to dry for a few hours and your Poké Ball will be ready to go!

BE SCISSOR SAFE!

Ask an adult to help you with the cutting stages.

Poké Ball Gallery
Need some artistic inspiration? Take a look at these amazing Poké Balls!

Poké Ball

Master Ball

Heal Ball

Luxury Ball

Repeat Ball

Ultra Ball

UNOVA POKÉDEX

ALOMOMOLA

TYPE: Water
HEIGHT: 1.2m
WEIGHT: 31.6kg
CATEGORY: Caring

Alomomola floats through ocean waters, enveloped in a special membrane. The Water-type uses the membrane to heal hurt Pokémon, enfolding the wounded species before taking it back to the shore. Alomomola has no known Evolutions.

AUDINO

TYPE: Normal
HEIGHT: 1.1m
WEIGHT: 31.0kg
CATEGORY: Hearing

Audino has a highly-developed sense of hearing that gives it a radar-like ability to sense movement and location from even the faintest of sounds. This Pokémon has curled feelers on each ear that it uses to detect people's feelings and listen to their heartbeat.

AXEW

TYPE: Dragon
HEIGHT: 0.6m
WEIGHT: 18.0kg
CATEGORY: Tusk

This Pokémon can be identified by the pointed tusk protruding from each side of its jaw. Axew uses its tusks to mark its territory and to crush berries for food. This Dragon-type evolves into Fraxure and then Haxorus.

DARMANITAN

TYPE: Fire
HEIGHT: 1.3m
WEIGHT: 92.9kg
CATEGORY: Blazing

Darmanitan draws its immense strength from an internal fire that blazes at over 1,400°C. It has the power to wreck a dump truck with a single punch. If weakened in combat, Darmanitan stands rigid like a statue and resorts to psychic attacks.

Are you ready to take your chances in Unova? You'll need to have facts at your fingertips so that you're ready to deal with the fascinating species that roam this diverse region. This brand new Pokédex is packed with some of Unova's most awesome native Pokémon. Research these crucial facts and stats, learn to recognise the species types and markings and you'll be sure to earn glory as a Trainer.

DARUMAKA

TYPE: Fire
HEIGHT: 0.6m
WEIGHT: 37.5kg
CATEGORY: Zen Charm

Darumaka produces droppings that are so hot, people in Unova used to tuck them inside their clothing to stay warm. This Pokémon is most active when its internal fire is burning, going to sleep when the flames subside. Darumaka evolves in Darmanitan.

DEERLING

TYPE: Normal-Grass
HEIGHT: 0.6m
WEIGHT: 19.5kg
CATEGORY: Season

Deerling's scent and fur change along with the turn of the seasons. The Pokémon's fur blends in with the mountain pastures, making it easier to hide if a predator comes near. This Normal-and Grass-type evolves into Sawsbuck.

DEWOTT

TYPE: Water
HEIGHT: 0.8m
WEIGHT: 24.5kg
CATEGORY: Discipline

Oshawott's evolved form trains very hard to perfect its flowing double-scalchop skills. Each Pokémon has developed its own unique technique, using the pair in a host of combat moves. It keeps the scalchops in tip-top condition.

DRILBUR

TYPE: Ground
HEIGHT: 0.3m
WEIGHT: 8.5kg
CATEGORY: Mole

Drilbur is an expert at drilling through ground, travelling at speeds of up to 50kph. It has been known to dig a channel as fast as a car motoring above the surface. To propel itself forward the Ground-type places its claws together and then spins.

DWEBBLE

TYPE: Bug-Rock
HEIGHT: 0.3m
WEIGHT: 14.5kg
CATEGORY: Rock Inn

Dwebble makes its home in a rock. If the rock breaks, the Pokémon won't rest until it finds a replacement that fits comfortably. The liquid from Dwebble's mouth can easily melt through stone.

EMOLGA

TYPE: Electric-Flying
HEIGHT: 0.4m
WEIGHT: 5.0kg
CATEGORY: Sky Squirrel

This sparky Pokémon generates electricity inside its cheek pouches, storing the charge in its cape-like membrane. When the membrane discharges the electricity, Emolga uses the power to fly. The Sky Squirrel Pokémon is not known to have any Evolutions.

EXCADRILL

TYPE: Ground-Steel
HEIGHT: 0.7m
WEIGHT: 40.4kg
CATEGORY: Subterrene

Drilbur's evolved form has a steel drill that can bore through iron plates. Although its underground activity is sometimes responsible for making holes in subway tunnels, Drilbur can also help builders with deep construction projects.

GALVANTULA

TYPE: Bug-Electric
HEIGHT: 0.8m
WEIGHT: 14.3kg
CATEGORY: EleSpider

This Pokémon uses its webs to great advantage. When a victim stumbles across its web the static in the thread shocks and immobilizes its prey, allowing Galvantula to devour the meal at its leisure. It can also spit out electrically-charged thread to protect itself when attacked.

KLINK

TYPE: Steel
HEIGHT: 0.3m
WEIGHT: 21.0kg
CATEGORY: Gear

Each Klink is made up of two interlocking minigears that rotate to create energy between them. Only the two right gears can mesh properly together, other gears will simply bounce off each other.

MINCCINO

TYPE: Normal
HEIGHT: 0.4m
WEIGHT: 5.8kg
CATEGORY: Chinchilla

Minccino keeps its habitat spotless, sweeping away dust and dirt with its broom-like tail. The Pokémon also uses its tail to acknowledge other Minccino, rubbing fur together in greeting. This Normal-type's tail is always clean and well-groomed.

MUNNA

TYPE: Psychic
HEIGHT: 0.6m
WEIGHT: 23.3kg
CATEGORY:
Dream Eater

Instead of walking on the ground, Munna transports itself by floating through the air. The Pokémon feeds on people's dreams, emitting a pinkish mist whenever it swallows a pleasant one. The sleeper will forget any dreams that get eaten by a passing Munna.

MUSHARNA

TYPE: Psychic
HEIGHT: 1.1m
WEIGHT: 60.5kg
CATEGORY: Drowsing

Musharna is the evolved form of Munna, a Psychic-type that trails a long mist from its forehead. The pink mist is composed of the dreams of people and other Pokémon. Musharna can even create the shape of things from the dreams that it has eaten.

OSHAWOTT

TYPE: Water
HEIGHT: 0.5m
WEIGHT: 5.9kg
CATEGORY: Sea Otter

Oshawott can detach the scalchop set on its belly, then wield it like a blade. The scalchop is made from the same material as claws. If threatened, Oschawott will slash at its attacker with the scalchop.

PANPOUR

TYPE: Water
HEIGHT: 0.6m
WEIGHT: 13.5kg
CATEGORY: Spray

Panpour does not thrive in a dry environment. The Pokémon stores moisture in its head tuft, spraying water out through its tail. The water inside its tuft is full of nutrients that can help plants grow.

PANSAGE

TYPE: Grass
HEIGHT: 0.6m
CATEGORY: 10.5kg
SPECIES: Grass Monkey

This Pokémon dwells in the depths of the forest. The leaves growing from Pansage's head are edible and known to have stress-relieving properties. When it encounters a tired-looking Pokémon, Pansage will share its leaves with them.

PANSEAR

TYPE: Fire
HEIGHT: 0.6m
WEIGHT: 11.0kg
CATEGORY: High Temp

Pansear can be recognized by the scarlet tuft on its head. Inside the tuft can burn at temperatures as hot as 300°C when the Fire-type gets angered. In calmer times, Pansear uses the tuft to roast berries for its meals. The Pokémon usually lives in volcanic caves.

PATRAT

TYPE: Normal
HEIGHT: 0.5m
WEIGHT: 11.6kg
CATEGORY: Scout

Patrat is a cautious Pokémon, anxiously guarding its nest in shifts so that there is always a lookout on duty. The Normal-type stores food in its cheek pouches, enabling it to keep watch for days at a time. Patrat evolves into Watchog.

PIDOVE

TYPE: Normal-Flying
HEIGHT: 0.3m
WEIGHT: 2.1kg
CATEGORY: Tiny Pigeon

This urban Pokémon is used to living amongst people, often flocking in great numbers in parks and municipal spaces. It evolves into Tranquill. Pidove is well-meaning, but sometimes finds it difficult to understand complex commands from its Trainer.

PIGNITE

TYPE: Fire-Fighting
HEIGHT: 1.0m
WEIGHT: 55.5kg
CATEGORY: Fire Pig

Pignite's appetite fuels the fire in its stomach. If it gets angry, the flames intensify so that the Pokémon can execute moves more swiftly and with greater force. However, Pignite gives off smoke in times of trouble. It is the evolved form of Tepig.

RESHIRAM

TYPE: Dragon-Fire
HEIGHT: 3.2m
WEIGHT: 330.0kg
CATEGORY: Vast White

Reshiram appears in many Unova legends. The Pokémon has a stunning white tail that exudes flame. The intense heat of this can sear everything in the surrounding area. Every time Reshiram's tail flares, the heat stirs the atmosphere and alters weather all over the world.

REUNICLUS

TYPE: Psychic
HEIGHT: 1.0m
WEIGHT: 20.1kg
CATEGORY: Multiplying

Reuniclus is highly-intelligent. This Pokémon fights by controlling arms with a grip strong enough to crush rock. When two Reuniclus shake hands, a link is created between their brains that increases their psychic power.

SANDILE

TYPE: Ground-Dark
HEIGHT: 0.7m
WEIGHT: 15.2kg
CATEGORY: Desert Croc

Even whilst moving, this Ground-and-Dark-type stays buried within the desert sands that it inhabits. Sandile sinks beneath the grains, only exposing its nose and eyes. The dark colouration around its eyes is a membrane that protects it from the sun's glare.

SCRAGGY

TYPE: Dark-Fighting
HEIGHT: 0.6m
WEIGHT: 11.8kg
CATEGORY: Shedding

Scraggy has a collar of rubbery skin around its neck that it can pull up to shield itself from attack. The Pokémon has an extremely thick skull and it is known to head-butt anyone that makes eye contact with it.

SERVINE

TYPE: Grass
HEIGHT: 0.8m
WEIGHT: 16.0kg
CATEGORY: Grass Snake

Servine uses rapid movements to trick its enemy, disappearing into thick vegetation to avoid confrontation. This Grass-type moves so effortlessly it almost appears to be gliding. The Pokémon is an expert at Vine Whip move attacks.

SEWADDLE

TYPE: Bug-Grass
HEIGHT: 0.3m
WEIGHT: 2.5kg
CATEGORY: Sewing

Sewaddle sleeps with its head hidden underneath its leaf-like hood. The Pokémon likes to stitch its own clothes. It chews up leaves then sews them together using a sticky thread that it produces out of its mouth. Sewaddle has six orange feet.

SNIVY

TYPE: Grass
HEIGHT: 0.6m
WEIGHT: 8.1kg
CATEGORY: Grass Snake

This Grass-type appears to slide across the ground. When Snivy basks its tail in sunshine, it photosynthesizes to become even more agile and quick. The Pokémon's tail droops when it feels unwell. Snivy evolves into Servine.

SWADLOON

TYPE: Bug-Grass
HEIGHT: 0.5m
WEIGHT: 7.3kg
CATEGORY:
Leaf-Wrapped

Swadloon naturally gathers in areas of rich forestation so that it can feed on fallen leaves which it turns into fertilizing nutrients to enrich the forests, causing lush foliage. When it feels cold, Swadloon wraps leaves around its body.

SWANNA

TYPE: Water-Flying
HEIGHT: 1.3m
WEIGHT: 24.2kg
CATEGORY: Keen Eye

Swanna is beautiful, but it can also be a fearsome opponent. When it fights, the Pokémon whips its neck round to deliver powerful jabs with its bill. At sunset, a flock of Swanna will perform a dance with their leader in the centre.

TEPIG

TYPE: Fire
HEIGHT: 0.5m
WEIGHT: 9.9kg
CATEGORY: Fire Pig

Tepig is able to blow fire out of its nose. This skill has a dual purpose – the fireballs can be used to blast an opponent or roast the berries it likes to eat. If the Fire-type catches a cold, its fire is reduced to black smoke. Tepig evolves into Pignite.

TRANQUILL

TYPE: Normal-Flying
HEIGHT: 0.6m
WEIGHT: 15.0kg
CATEGORY: Wild Pigeon

Tranquill is a natural navigator – if it gets separated from its Trainer it will always be able to find its way back to them, no matter how far they have travelled. Many people believe that the forest home of wild Tranquill is a place without war.

WATCHOG

TYPE: Normal
HEIGHT: 1.1m
WEIGHT: 27.0kg
CATEGORY: Lookout

Watchog stands high on its back legs when it sees a predator coming its way. It responds to danger by spitting out the berry seeds it stores in its cheeks and making the patterns on its body glow. Watchog has amazing eyesight. It can even see in the dark.

WOOBAT

TYPE: Psychic-Flying
HEIGHT: 0.4m
WEIGHT: 2.1kg
CATEGORY: Bat

Woobat relies on the ultrasonic waves that it emits from its nose. When it flies around dark caves and forests, its nose sends out waves that help it judge distances and chase prey. When it's time to go to sleep, Woobat uses the suction of its nostrils to grip cavern walls.

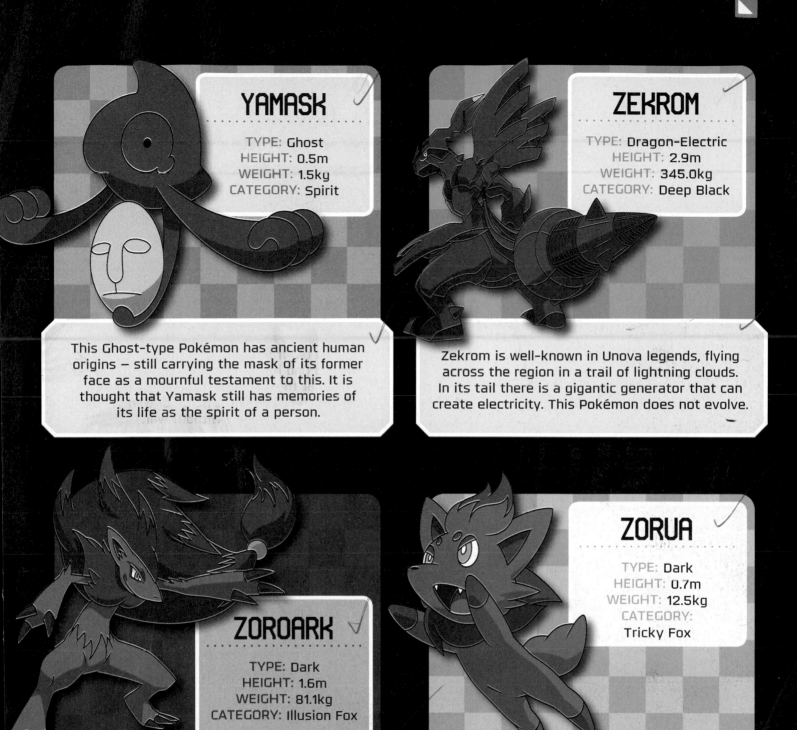

YAMASK

TYPE: Ghost
HEIGHT: 0.5m
WEIGHT: 1.5kg
CATEGORY: Spirit

This Ghost-type Pokémon has ancient human origins – still carrying the mask of its former face as a mournful testament to this. It is thought that Yamask still has memories of its life as the spirit of a person.

ZEKROM

TYPE: Dragon-Electric
HEIGHT: 2.9m
WEIGHT: 345.0kg
CATEGORY: Deep Black

Zekrom is well-known in Unova legends, flying across the region in a trail of lightning clouds. In its tail there is a gigantic generator that can create electricity. This Pokémon does not evolve.

ZOROARK

TYPE: Dark
HEIGHT: 1.6m
WEIGHT: 81.1kg
CATEGORY: Illusion Fox

Zoroark form strong bonds with each other, using trickery to protect the safety of their pack. The Pokémon can transform into its opponents and deceive entire groups of people. It uses illusion to hide the location of its lair. Zoroark has a distinctive mane of red and black.

ZORUA

TYPE: Dark
HEIGHT: 0.7m
WEIGHT: 12.5kg
CATEGORY:
Tricky Fox

Zorua is the pre-evolved form of Zoroark. It is said to take on the form of a silent child, but it can actually transform itself into many different guises. If necessary, it can even change itself into the shape of its opponent in order to take others by surprise.

LIAR LIAR

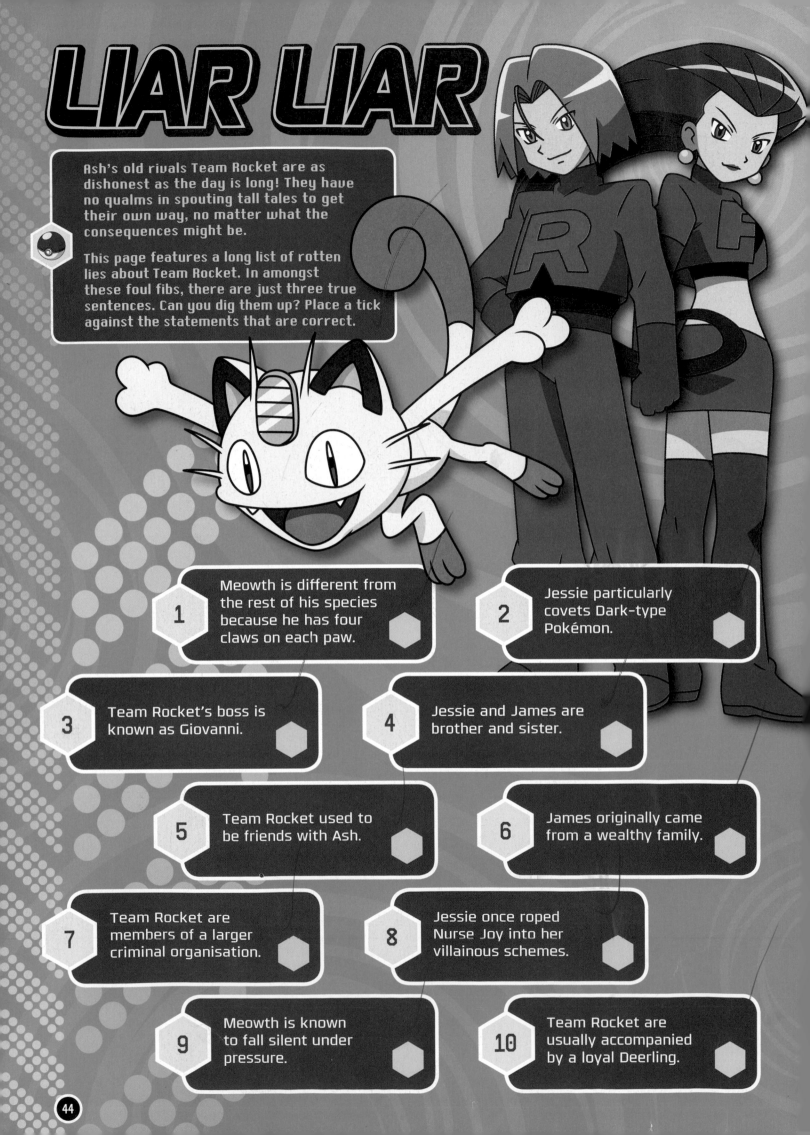

Ash's old rivals Team Rocket are as dishonest as the day is long! They have no qualms in spouting tall tales to get their own way, no matter what the consequences might be.

This page features a long list of rotten lies about Team Rocket. In amongst these foul fibs, there are just three true sentences. Can you dig them up? Place a tick against the statements that are correct.

1 Meowth is different from the rest of his species because he has four claws on each paw.

2 Jessie particularly covets Dark-type Pokémon.

3 Team Rocket's boss is known as Giovanni.

4 Jessie and James are brother and sister.

5 Team Rocket used to be friends with Ash.

6 James originally came from a wealthy family.

7 Team Rocket are members of a larger criminal organisation.

8 Jessie once roped Nurse Joy into her villainous schemes.

9 Meowth is known to fall silent under pressure.

10 Team Rocket are usually accompanied by a loyal Deerling.

Axew ATTACK!

Iris is a budding Trainer, just like Ash! She is joined on her travels by Axew, a big-hearted Dragon-type that likes to ride in her hair. Axew has still got a lot to learn about battling, but it's ready to defend Iris no matter what comes their way.

Can you find the missing pieces to complete this knockout shot of Iris and Axew? Draw a line to match the right shapes to the gaps in the picture, or find a pen and draw the pieces back in place.

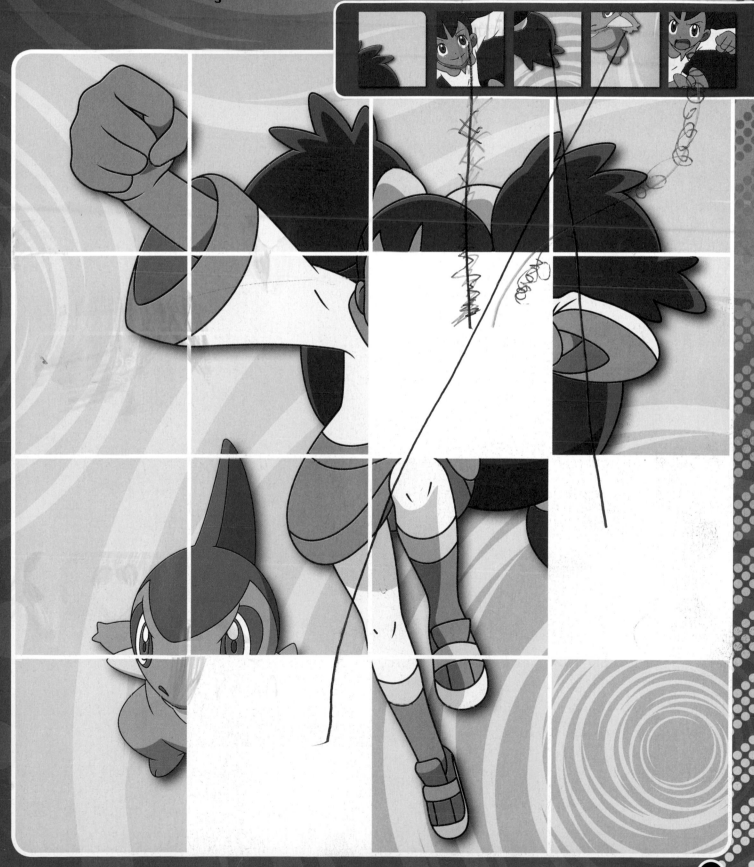

POKÉMON™
COLOURING

Watch out,
Unova - Ash, Iris
and Cilan are on
their way!

Bring this
awesome
colouring poster
to life using
your favourite
crayons or
felt-tips.

THE BATTLE CLUB AND TEPIG'S CHOICE!

Continuing his Unova region journey as part of his quest to become a Pokémon Master, Ash has sets his sights on the Striaton City Gym. The determined Trainer is more than ready to take on a new Gym Leader in his first Gym battle…

Ash and Iris stood at the top of the hillside, looking down at the high-rises and houses sprawled out below.

"Yes!" cried Ash. "We've finally reached Striaton City. Now it's time for a Gym battle…"

Iris snorted and shook her head.

"Not quite Ash," she replied. "This is Accumula Town. Striaton City is the next town over! But of course you wouldn't know that, you're a kid!"

Ash groaned with frustration. He was psyched and ready to make his mark in the Unova region. Getting this far had been a long and eventful journey and he still hadn't made it to Striaton City!

When Iris saw Ash's face fall, even she couldn't help feeling a little sorry for him.

"Why don't you go to the Pokémon Battle Club?" she suggested. "That's where I'm going."

Iris led Ash down the hill, into the heart of Accumula Town. Soon the pair were standing outside a modern glass fronted-building with a Pokémon battle symbol emblazoned above its doors.

The friends walked into the lobby of the Pokémon Battle Club. Inside, there was a smart line of computer screens – online bulletin boards that visiting Trainers were free to log on to.

Iris selected a screen, then clicked onto the network.

"Each Trainer enters their Pokémon's profile as well as the type of Pokémon that they want to battle against," explained Iris. "It's an awesome place for Trainers to sharpen their skills by battling as they see fit!"

"Wow," grinned Ash. "Alright!"

Iris, Ash and Pikachu entered the Pokémon Battle Club training area. The doors opened onto a large battle arena where two boys were standing face-to-face.

"Perfect timing," trilled Iris, clapping her hands. "Looks like they're just about to start battling!"

Ash held his Pokédex up to scan the Trainers' battle choices. An impressive-looking Servine flanked one boy, the other had called out a Dewott.

SERVINE

THE GRASS SNAKE POKÉMON
The evolved form of Snivy. Servine whips its opponents with vines and dodges their attacks by hiding in the shadows of thick foliage.

DEWOTT

THE DISCIPLINE POKÉMON
The evolved form of Oshawott. Through rigid training, Dewott uses the double scalchop technique to accomplish its fluid swordsmanship.

Ash and Iris took a seat at the side of the arena, but this clash was destined to be short and decisive. Within seconds, the Dewott had used an awesome Water Gun attack to stop Servine in its tracks!

A man with a bushy moustache declared the battle over.

"Servine, are you OK?" asked his Trainer, helping his Pokémon to its feet. The Servine nodded its head and the Trainer picked him up and carried him out to get healed.

"Welcome!" said the man, noticing Iris and Ash. "We're here to take care of all your battle needs. My name is Don George and I'm the Battle Manager."

Ash stepped forward and Iris introduced him to Don George.

"Iris was telling me that anyone could have a battle here if they wanted to," he said. "I wanna get ready to make a challenge at the Striaton City Gym!"

Don George nodded. "That's true!"

Before Ash could ask any more questions, the boy with the Dewott interrupted.

"Excuse me," he began, "but is that Pikachu yours? Would you like to have a Pokémon battle with me?"

Ash didn't hesitate. "You're on!"

Pikachu was getting ready to battle when Ash's Oshawott appeared beside him. Iris gulped – it wasn't meant to come out of its Poké Ball on its own like that!

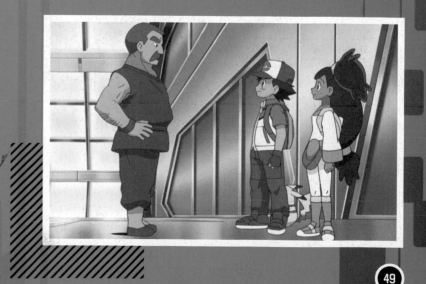

Even though it hadn't been summoned by Ash, it seemed that his Oshawott was determined to battle! The plucky little Pokémon shoved Pikachu out of the way and then puffed itself up to its full height.

"Dewott!" shouted the boy. "Let's go!"

Suddenly Oshawott didn't seem so tough. The fearsome sight of Dewott on the rampage sent Ash's new recruit straight back to its Poké Ball!

"Now that's settled," said Ash. "Pikachu, use Thunderbolt!"

The battle was fast and furious from the get-go. Pikachu's blasts of electricity were expertly dodged by Dewott, although its Iron Tail move hit the Water-type hard. The arena shook and rumbled with the force of the exchange.

Iris watched intently, nodding her head in admiration when Dewott executed a knockout Razor Shell attack.

Not so far away from Ash and his friends, Team Rocket were creeping around the outbuildings at the back of the Pokémon Battle Center.

"Good," whispered Jessie, realising that the coast was clear.

The threesome tiptoed in through the storage room door, delighted that someone had been careless enough to leave the place unlocked. Inside boxes were stacked from floor to ceiling.

"This affords us with the opportunity we need to stock up on supplies," smirked James.

Meowth was about to slash a hole in the first box, when something flew past him. The trio recoiled in surprise, setting off the storage room's alarm system.

"Not good!" screeched Jessie.

"Ex-it!" barked James.

Dewott was going in with its double scalchops when the alarm began to ring. Within moments, a group of site staff appeared in the lift.

"Battle Manager, Sir!" cried the leader. "Something's in the storage room!"

"It's probably that mystery Pokémon!" added his colleague.

Don George turned to Ash and his rival.

"The battle will have to be suspended for now."

A mystery Pokémon? That sounded exciting! Ash decided to go and check it out. He and Iris followed Don George into the Battle Club's security office. Inside, one of the sub-managers was already checking out the storage room on the CCTV.

"It doesn't look like much was stolen," he reported.

"The security camera must have recorded something," replied Don George. "Let's review it!"

The sub-manager tracked the footage back. Don George explained that so much food had been stolen from the storage room recently, they'd found it necessary to set up a state of the art security system! Although they hadn't tracked down the thief yet, the rise of unidentified Pokémon sightings had given them hope that there might be a new species in the area!

UMBREON
THE MOONLIGHT POKÉMON
An evolved form of Eevee. The rings on Umbreon's body glow faintly when exposed to the moon's aura and it gains a mysterious power.

When the sub-manager ran the tape, there was a double surprise. Ash immediately recognised the trespassers as Team Rocket, but they also spotted the shadow of a Pokémon dashing past the camera. It was gone in the blink of an eye.

"Dark and skinny," mused Iris. "What kind of Pokémon is that?"

Ash flicked through his Pokédex and then flashed a screen at his friend.

"Looks to me like this..."

"That's so cool!" gasped Iris, seriously impressed.

"But Umbreon don't normally live in the Unova region," said Don George. "If we discovered one it would be a huge find. Let's keep our eyes open and find this Pokémon!"

"Ash!" whispered Iris. "What do you say we go and help them out?"

Ash didn't need asking twice – he was in!

Ash and Iris ran outside with Don George and his security team.

"Search every inch of this place!" cried the Battle Manager. "Where could that Umbreon have gone?"

While the security guards raked through bushes and outbuildings, Team Rocket peeped out from behind a wall.

"While they're looking for Umbreon," sniggered Meowth, "we'll stock up on supplies to our heart's content!"

Jessie's eyes lit up. Quick as a flash she reached in her bag and produced a can of paint.

"This paint will allow Umbreon to lure those guys far, far away," she schemed.

It only took a few minutes for Jessie and James to paint Meowth in black and yellow. The smart-talking Pokémon sauntered round to the front of the Pokémon Battle Club, putting on his best Umbreon impression.

"That's right boys!" he called. "It's me…"

Don George and his men tore after Meowth, leaving the Battle Club wide open for Jessie and James.

At the back of the Pokémon Battle Club, Ash and Iris had decided to lay out a food trail for the Umbreon to follow. They set down a line of Pokémon food bowls from the main building to the storage room.

"I think we should split up so we can keep an eye on this place," whispered Iris. "I'm planning to catch it, if you don't mind!"

"She would say that," groaned Ash, watching her skip away.

Suddenly Oshawott re-appeared from its Poké Ball. It began jumping up and down next to Pikachu.

"You wanna help out, huh?" grinned Ash. "OK. You and Pikachu guard this area!"

The Trainer headed off to his lookout post, leaving his Pokémon in the storage room. Instead of keeping watch however, Oshawott started eating the bowls of Pokémon food!

When Pikachu told it off, Oshawott barged him into a stack of boxes. A series of boxes plummeted down onto Pikachu's head, knocking the Electric-type out, the final box covering the Pokémon completely.

Ash was walking off to find more Pokémon food, when he noticed a dark shadow flitting towards the storage room. It had to be the mystery Pokémon!

"Yes!" he whispered. "It's about time, Umbreon!"

Startled by Ash's voice, the mystery Pokémon stopped for an instant and turned. The shadowy figure was small, with a round snout and a curly tail.

"Hold on!" gasped Ash. "That's not Umbreon..."

Ash stared down at his Pokédex – a Tepig was one of the three Pokémon a new Trainer could choose in the Unova region. This Tepig looked so skinny and dirty – no wonder they'd thought it was Umbreon!

"It's got a rope tangled round its snout!" cried Ash. "That must make it hard for Tepig to eat!"

Tepig gave a nervous snort and then made a bolt for cover. Ash ran after it.

By the time Iris arrived on the scene, Ash was holding Tepig in his arms.

"I won't hurt you," soothed Ash, as the terrified Pokémon struggled to wriggle free.

Poouuff!

Tepig blasted Ash with a cloud of sooty black smoke. Ash coughed, but didn't flinch.

"I told you I won't hurt you," he smiled.

Iris fetched a bowl of Pokémon food, while Ash tried to pull the cord off Tepig's snout. It was stuck pretty tight.

"Be gentle!" said Iris. "Who could do such a terrible thing?" asked Ash.

When the rope was finally free, the little Tepig tucked into the food. The Pokémon gobbled up the snack in no time!

TEPIG

THE FIRE PIG POKÉMON

Normally fire shoots out of Tepig's snout, but it shoots out smoke instead when it's feeling ill.

On the other side of Accumula Town, Don George and his men were finally catching up with Meowth.

"I guess the jig is up," he panted, skidding into a dead end.

Don George cornered Meowth against a wall, desperate to finally behold the mysterious creature that had been visiting the Pokémon Battle Club.

"To think that we've found the first Umbreon," gushed the Battle Manager, welling up with emotion. "The very first Umbreon to ever be discovered in the Unova region! I'll never forget this moment!"

The over-awed sub-managers started to snivel too.

"This discovery will go down in history!" claimed one.

"It will be written up in the schoolbooks!" decided another.

The third was sobbing so hard he could only stammer. "Catch it, I'm begging you!"

Meowth was taken aback. Seeing the men's excitement was leading him on a serious guilt trip!

"Excuse me," said Meowth quietly. "I hate to take the wind out of your sails, but I'm not Umbreon."

Don George was flabbergasted.

Meowth rubbed at the paint, exposing the gold panel on his forehead.

"See my charm?" he explained. "That proves that I'm just a Meowth, passing by…"

Don George dropped to his knees and cried in disappointment.

"You're just a talking Meowth!" wailed the Battle Manager, leaving the coast clear for the Pokémon to slip away.

It was only when Meowth had gone, that one of the sub-managers realised what they'd just witnessed.

"Excuse me, Battle Manager?" he said. "Wouldn't a talking Meowth be considered rare as well?"

Don George nodded, beating his chest in frustration. This was a double calamity!

While Ash and his friends were chasing after the mystery Pokémon, Jessie and James sneaked back to the storage room. This time, Team Rocket had taken the precaution of cutting the alarm system wires.

"I'll stay here and keep watch," decided Jessie, posting herself in the doorway.

James stalked in and started rifling through boxes. He tossed empty cartons of Pokémon food aside, but then he hit the jackpot. There, under an upturned box, was Ash's Pikachu! James couldn't believe his luck.

"There's no doubt!" gasped Jessie. "This is the twerp's Pokémon."

"What in the world is it doing passed out inside a box?" wondered James.

"It doesn't matter," snapped Jessie. "Think how pleased the Boss will be with our hard work!"

Unaware of his best pal's predicament, Ash carried Tepig round to the entrance of the Pokémon Battle Club to show Don George.

"Hi!" shouted the Battle Manager. "We thought we found Umbreon, but it was a complete hoax."

"Look at this!" grinned Ash. "The shadow turned out to be Tepig instead."

Don George took a good look at the Pokémon – he'd seen this Tepig before!

"A Trainer who once visited our Battle Club abandoned it when it lost its battle," he explained. "He simply tied it to a stake and left, saying that he had no use for a weak Pokémon. I tried to free Tepig, but it chewed itself loose and disappeared before I could get to it!"

Ash grimaced. He couldn't understand how anyone could do something so terrible to a Pokémon they were travelling and battling with!

"If I ever meet that Trainer," vowed Iris. "I'll teach him a lesson he'll never forget!"

The triumphant Team Rocket chose that moment to creep round the corner. Oshawott followed looking agitated and gestured at Team Rocket.

"What's going on?" demanded Don George.

Ash checked the black sack slung over Jessie's shoulder. He'd recognise the squeaks coming from that sack anywhere. Pikachu had to be inside!

"Give me back my Pikachu!" he bellowed.

"How could you abandon your Pokémon?" sneered Jessie. "You're a Trainer of the lowest order!"

James flicked a button, encasing the dastardly trio in a glassy escape pod.

"Now we've got owner's rights!" he simpered. "Goodbye, twerp!"

Ash kicked the ground in fury. "Come back!"

Oshawott tried to stop the thieves with a Water Gun attack, but it was easily repelled.

Team Rocket jeered and cackled as their pod lifted up into air. Don George and his men gasped in shock to see the talking Meowth they'd encountered earlier waving down at them.

Ash was desperately trying to figure out what to do, when the little Tepig started to snort at him.

"Tepig?" he gasped. "Do you want to help?"

It was worth a shot – Team Rocket and Pikachu were disappearing fast!

"Alright Tepig," shouted Ash. "Use Ember!"

The brave Fire-type summoned all its strength, blasting Team Rocket with an astonishing jet of fire sparks. The escape pod instantly disintegrated, sending its occupiers crashing to the ground. Ash leapt forward to catch Pikachu in his arms.

"Tepig, thanks a lot!" he cried. "You helped save Pikachu!"

Iris and the Battle Club men cheered and clapped. While the good guys celebrated, Team Rocket soared across the horizon in their emergency gliders. The hapless crooks needed to escape before the heat got turned up any higher! As they made their getaway, the trio vowed to catch-up with Pikachu again soon.

Iris was super-impressed with Tepig's show of strength.

"You're a cutie," she squealed. "I'd better catch you!"

The Trainer got out her Poké Ball but Tepig shook its head to say no. Iris groaned – why did this keep happening when Ash was around?

Don George had the answer.

"It appears Tepig has chosen Ash as his Trainer!" he explained. "After all its hardships, Tepig knows a great Trainer when it sees one."

"So Tepig?" laughed Ash. "Wanna come with me?"

The little Pokémon nodded, making its intentions pretty clear.

"Awesome!" replied Ash. "Alright Poké Ball, let's go!"

There was a blast of light as the Trainer hurled the Poké Ball towards his new charge. Tepig instantly disappeared inside, the latest recruit to the Ketchum team!

"Yes!" cheered Ash. "I caught a Tepig!"

Once Tepig was safely tucked in its Poké Ball, Ash crouched down to catch up with Pikachu.

"Remember what Team Rocket told me?" he said. "What were you doing inside a box?"

Pikachu scampered forward to relay the whole sorry story. The Trainer can't fully understand the complicated story of what had happened in the storage room after he'd left! Oshawott sighed with relief when Ash made it clear that it wasn't in any trouble.

"I think it's time we head off to the Striaton Gym," he announced, "with our new friend Tepig!"

So Ash's plan to challenge the Striaton City Gym takes an unexpected turn! Only time will tell how that might affect the kind of strategy our hero will be using… see the next story on page 64!

Pokémon BATTLE CLUB!

How would you fare at the Pokémon Battle Club? As the Battle Manager, Don George likes to check out all the Trainers that turn up to take on new rivals and hone their fighting skills.

As well as being fearless and quick-thinking, the most promising Trainers work hard to build up an extensive bank of Pokémon knowledge. Understanding a Pokémon's behaviour is vital for success in the Battle Gym!

Test your knowledge in this Pokémon quiz. As a rookie in the Unova region, can you bag a score that would impress Don George?

What happens to the food that Pignite consumes?

a. It fuels the fire in its belly ✓

b. It is spat back at its opponents ☐

c. It is smoked until it takes on the flavour that Pignite likes ☐

(1)

What type of Pokémon is Oshawott?

a. Normal ☐

b. Fighting ☐

c. Water ✓

(2)

What is the name of this Pokémon?

a. Zorua ☐

b. Reuniclus ☐

c. Alomomola ✓

(3)

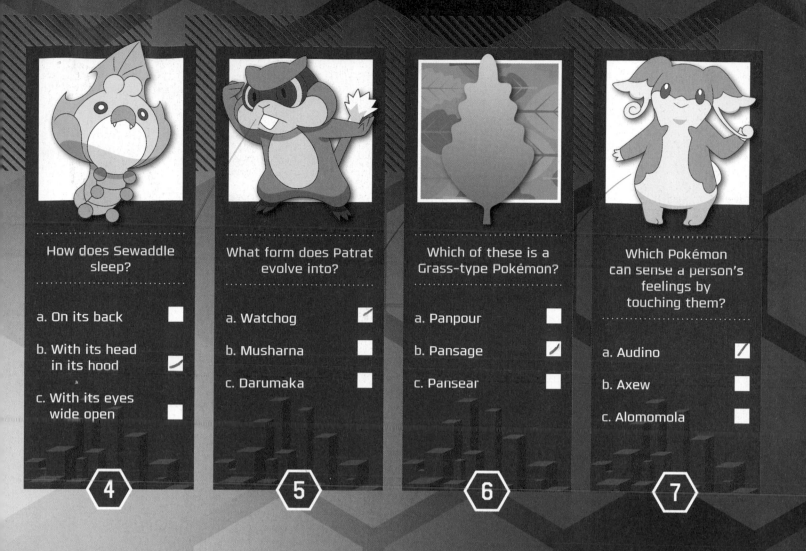

How does Sewaddle sleep?

a. On its back ☐

b. With its head in its hood ☑

c. With its eyes wide open ☐

4

What form does Patrat evolve into?

a. Watchog ☑

b. Musharna ☐

c. Darumaka ☐

5

Which of these is a Grass-type Pokémon?

a. Panpour ☐

b. Pansage ☑

c. Pansear ☐

6

Which Pokémon can sense a person's feelings by touching them?

a. Audino ☑

b. Axew ☐

c. Alomomola ☐

7

Which of these Pokémon is not native to the Unova region?

a. Darmanitan ☐

b. Tranquill ☐

c. Umbreon ☑

8

This is a close-up of which Pokémon?

a. Emolga ☐

b. Pidove ☐

c. Swanna ☑

9

Which of these Pokémon does not feature in Unova legends?

a. Reshiram ☐

b. Zoroark ☑

c. Zekrom ☐

10

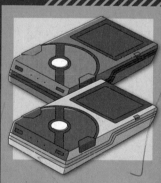

Finding it tough?

Turn to page 34 for a little extra help – every Trainer should have their Pokédex on hand when they need it!

MISSING POKÉMON

This brain-bashing puzzle will test your problem-solving and sketching skills at the same time! This grid is full of Normal-type Pokémon, but each species features just once in each column and row. Test your logic by working out which Pokémon should appear in each blank space. Carefully draw each one in place.

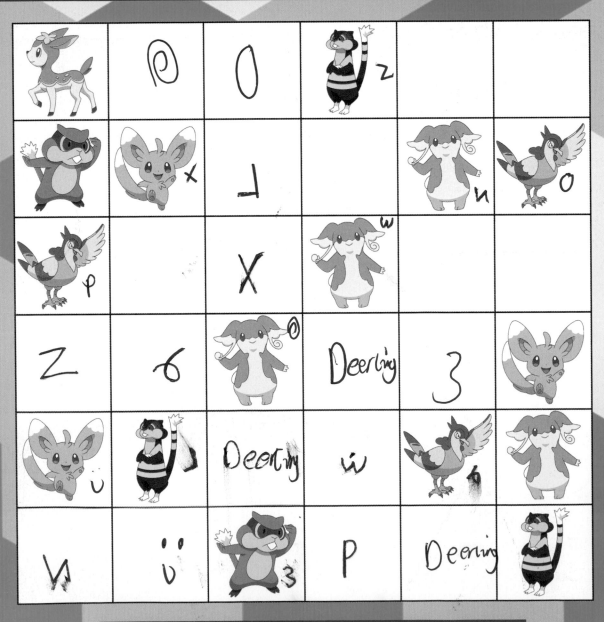

All finished? Check your answers on page 77.

GALVANTULA
COLOUR COPY

Galvantula makes an intimidating sight, crawling out from its electrically-charged web! Entice the EleSpider Pokémon onto this Annual page by carefully copying the panels from the top grid into the matching ones in the blank web below.

When you've finished drawing, colour Galvantula in using shades of mustard and plum.

CODED CARVINGS

Take a look at the inscription on this old tablet. The Pokémon's secrets have been recorded in an ancient letter code.

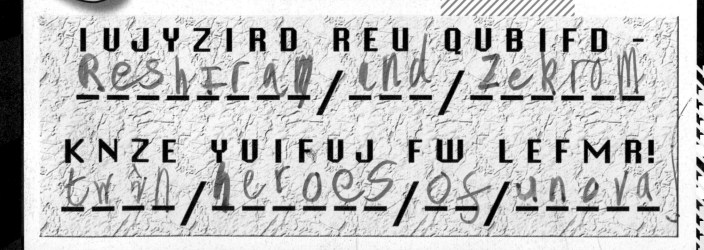

IUJYZIRD REU QUBIFD -
Reshiram and Zekrom

KNZE YUIFUJ FW LEFMR!
twin heroes of unova

Ancient writings and fireside tales have long talked about two Legendary Pokémon - one brilliant white, the other as dark as night. It is said that each of these giants can wield awesome power, from lightning bolts to flames hot enough to scorch vast tracts of earth.

Use the key to help you decipher the code and then write the meaning of the carving in the panel opposite.

CODE KEY:	A = R	H = Y	O = F	U = M
	B = S	I = Z	P = G	W = N
	C = T	J = A	Q = H	X = O
	D = U	K = B	R = I	Y = P
	E = V	L = C	S = J	Z = Q
	F = W	M = D	T = K	
	G = X	N = E	U = L	

SNIVY PLAYS HARD TO CATCH!

After winning the Trio Badge at the Striaton Gym, Ash is on his way to Nacrene City! His new friends Iris and Cilan are there to share the journey, but it seems that there's a pressing situation that needs some attention first...

"Man!" groaned Ash, clutching his belly. "I need food and quick!"

"Why don't we stop here for lunch?" suggested Iris. "You wait here and I'll get things ready."

Ash, Cilan and Pikachu gathered round an old tree stump, while Iris leapt into action. The agile young Trainer was an expert at roaming through woodland, hunting out the most delicious fruits and berries to pick.

Within moments she was back, proudly setting a bowl on the tree stump piled high with fresh produce. "Wow does that look good!" grinned Ash, reaching for a tasty pear.

Iris nodded. "Lunch here we come!"

"Hold on!" cried Cilan, whisking the bowl out of their hands. "Just a minute."

Ash, Iris and Pikachu watched open-mouthed as their friend tied an apron round his waist and then got peeling, chopping and cooking. The tantalising smell of bubbling fruit soon wafted around the forest.

"Is it ready yet?" asked Ash. "I'm starved!"

"Sorry for the wait," smiled Cilan. "Here you go!"

The Gym Leader held out two plates of fruit muffins and cakes.

Iris sniffed at the treats, making a point of telling the boys how she only ate fresh fruit.

"Only a kid would make a big deal out of this," she muttered, reluctantly taking a bite. Iris's eyes widened. It was a taste sensation!

"Cilan!" she gasped. "You are a master chef!"

Ash chuckled, popping in another cake. "She's right there!"

"If I can eat food like this every day," decided Iris, "maybe travelling with you two won't be too bad!"

Cilan took that as a compliment, offering Iris and Ash seconds. The Trainers made a bolt for the stove, but when they looked there was nothing there.

"That doesn't make sense," said Cilan. "There was plenty of food there a second ago, I'm sure of it."

Ash looked around. Apart from them, the forest path was deserted. "What in the world can have happened to it?" wondered Iris.

Suddenly, something rustled in the long grass on the other side of the track. Ash and Pikachu ran over to take a closer look.

"Hey, that's a Snivy!" whispered Ash, pointing to the elegant green Pokémon that was stood in front of him, still clutching one of Cilan's fruit muffins. "It's one of the three starter Pokémon you can get in the Unova region. I'm gonna catch it now!"

Ash pulled out a Poké Ball and threw it at Snivy.

"Did you get it?' asked Iris.

Ash nodded proudly, but Snivy was only captive for an instant. It quickly repelled the Poké Ball, sending it spinning back into the Trainer's hand.

"If Snivy went into your Poké Ball like that, then it must be a wild Pokémon," cried Iris.

"She's right," agreed Cilan.

Ash was already pushing his way through the grass, chasing after Snivy.

"You're gonna be my Pokémon soon!" he laughed. "No doubt!"

As soon as he caught up with Snivy again, Ash sent Pikachu in with Quick Attack. Pikachu powered through the grasses, but the Pokémon simply dodged the Electric-type!

"Ash," warned Cilan. "Snivy are really smart and speedy Pokémon. Not easy to catch!"

Snivy flashed a satisfied look at Ash and Pikachu.

"It looks like you're being made fun of!" giggled Iris.

"What?" yelled Ash. "Pikachu, use Thunderbolt!"

Pikachu's eyes filled with determination, ready to wield a mighty Thunderbolt attack. Snivy watched for a moment, before radiating a powerful energy that seemed to mesmerise Ash's best friend.

"What's up with Pikachu?" gasped the Trainer.

"Pikachu got hit by Snivy's Attract!" replied Iris.

Cilan explained that Attract causes the infatuation of Pokémon of the opposite gender.

"It worked on Pikachu so this Snivy must be a girl," smirked Iris. "Oh boy Ash, don't you even know that? What a kid!"

Ash shot a fierce look at Iris, then leapt in front of Pikachu – now Snivy was attacking his pal with Vine Whip!

"Are you OK, Pikachu?" asked Ash, shielding the Electric-type from harm.

Snivy retracted its vines, shocked at the sight of such tenderness between a Trainer and his Pokémon. In a sudden whirl of activity, Snivy disappeared using its Leaf Storm move.

Ash leapt to his feet, but the Pokémon had already got away.

"Incredible!" marvelled Cilan. "Snivy's moves are really high level!"

Iris had a theory.

"I wonder if it abandoned its Trainer?"

"What does that mean?" asked Ash.

"Snivy are intelligent," retorted Iris. "I've heard that if they have a really bad Trainer, they'll leave them."

Cilan agreed. "I wouldn't be surprised if Snivy did just that!"

Ash's eyes filled with excitement – now he wanted that Snivy more than ever!

"That's it!" he shouted. "There's no doubt that I'm going to catch that Pokémon, eh Pikachu?"

Ash's friend chattered in agreement, its ears alert and ready for the chase.

"Can't the two of you just calm down?" sighed Iris.

"Iris, this is no time for calming down!" yelled Ash, reaching for his Poké Ball.

Ash released Pidove from the Poké Ball and it wheeled in wide circles above the travellers' heads.

"Pidove!" called Ash. "Go and find Snivy!"

Just a few metres further up the track, Team Rocket were gathered in the gloomy opening of a cave. An open suitcase was propped up in front of them, displaying a laptop screen.

"I have some important information for you..." Jessie, James and Meowth moved in closer. On the screen, their boss Giovanni was relaying a critical new brief.

"The secret organisation in the Unova region is commencing operations," he warned. "They may in fact already be aware of our presence in the area. Be on your highest alert!"

"Understood!" barked the trio.

The laptop screen went black, ending Giovanni's latest transmission.

"Secret organisation," mused Jessie. "I wonder who they are?"

"Whatever the deal is," decided Meowth. "We better be extra careful!"

"Right now it is imperative that we work to strengthen our offensive power," added James. "And that means catching more Pokémon right away!"

As luck would have it, Jessie noticed something twitch in the grasses outside the cave.

"It's a Snivy!" she grinned, eyes lighting up.

"Sound perfect!" agreed James. "Let's capture Snivy first thing."

Jessie tossed a Poké Ball at the fleeing Pokémon, but Snivy gracefully eluded it, back-flipping over the top.

"Meowth!" hissed Jessie. "It's up to you!"

Meowth brandished his fearsome claws, razor-sharp edges gleaming in the sunlight.

"Time to use Scratch!" he hissed.

The fast-talking Pokémon leapt after the Snivy, paws flashing through the air at lightning speed. Meowth stopped to admire his ruthless handiwork and gasped. Instead of attacking Snivy, he'd only managed to etch a few notches on a nearby rock!

"There's no way!" he spat, but his quarry had already gone.

Snivy darted into the rocky mountain range that loomed above the trail, losing itself amongst the craggy peaks. When it was sure that it was out of danger, it curled up to rest.

The weary Pokémon was dreaming about its intriguing encounter with Ash when Pidove glided overhead. Pidove made its distinctive call to alert the Trainer of its discovery.

"Awesome!" cried Ash. "Thanks for finding Snivy! Come on Pikachu, let's step on it!"

Ash, Iris and Cilan ran along the path and then picked their way up to the rocky outpost where Pidove was circling.

"Snivy!" called the psyched Trainer. "I wanna battle you again!"

The Grass-type slowly woke up, gliding to the cliff-edge to peer at the approaching group.

Suddenly Oshawott burst out of its Poké Ball.

"Hold on," said Ash. "You mean that you want to battle Snivy this time?"

Oshawott nodded solemnly, determined to prove its worthiness to the Trainer.

Ash gave the OK for Oshawott to battle, but before anything could happen a bombardment of rocks plummeted down the side of the mountain – Snivy had purposely swept the boulders over the edge with its tail!

Ash and his Pokémon ducked behind a large rock, just in the nick of time. As the dust settled, they clambered back up to the cliff edge.

"We're not giving up that easily!" he chuckled, determined to take Snivy on.

Snivy's big brown eyes were transfixed on Ash as he allowed Oshawott to step forward.

"I'm catching you this time Snivy," he promised. "Just watch!"

"Oshawott!" ordered Ash. "Water Gun. Go!"

Oshawott sprang into action, ready to give its best shot. As it locked in combat with Snivy, Iris and Cilan made it to the scene.

"Hey!" wailed Iris. "Why is Ash battling using Oshawott? Doesn't he know that a Water-type has a disadvantage against a Grass-type?"

"Not so loud," breathed the Trainer. "Of course I know that!"

"Ash is an interesting guy," smiled Cilan. "It must be Oshawott's enthusiasm that convinced him."

Snivy countered Ash's Pokémon with Vine Whip, but Oshawott managed to dodge it just in time. The intrepid Water-type pulled out its scalchop. It was about to spin it at Snivy when a devoted expression clouded its vision.

"Man!" scowled Ash. "Snivy's used Attract again!"

From that moment on, Oshawott was an easy target for the accomplished Snivy. Ash was shrewd enough to recall Oshawott to its Poké Ball before any more damage could be done.

Snivy skimmed along the rock face at astonishing speed, then dropped down into the forest below.

"Pidove!" shouted Ash. "Keep following Snivy!"

It was a struggle for the Trainer to keep up, but there was no way that Ash was going to give in now! Iris and Cilan struggled behind, watching the drama unfold.

"Why can't Ash just give it a rest already?" demanded Iris. "I've never seen anyone more stubborn."

Cilan chuckled to himself.

"I think the more correct word would be 'determined'."

As the forest canopy got thicker, Snivy switched from the ground to the trees. It swung effortlessly from branch to branch, floating high above Ash's head.

"Hop on board, Pikachu," said the Trainer. "Snivy's all mine!"

The gutsy kid decided to take a leaf out of Snivy's book, reaching out for the nearest vine. Pikachu clung to Ash's neck, peering through the branches at the Pokémon flitting ahead.

With a mighty effort, Ash grasped vine after vine, building up momentum as he moved through the trees.

Cr-ack!

The vine that the Trainer was clinging to snapped, sending both him and Pikachu plummeting into a boggy swamp! Ash's fall was broken by a giant lily pad, but now he was stranded there.

"Are you OK, Pikachu?" Ash asked gently.

Snivy watched through the trees as the Trainer checked his best friend over from ears to tail.

"Uh-oh!" groaned Ash. "We're starting to sink!"

The lily pad was quickly taking on mud and water. Ash helped Pikachu climb onto his head, careful to keep his precious Pokémon out of harm.

The lily pad began to sink lower and lower into the bog. Soon Ash was up to his chest in mud. The swamp water was too gloopy to swim through — for the moment at least, the Trainer was forced to put his hunt for Snivy on emergency hold!

Suddenly a thick vine flew across the surface of the swamp. Ash was relieved to see Iris and Cilan clinging to the other end.

"Hurry Ash!" called Iris. "Grab onto this!"

"Thanks a lot you two!" grinned Ash, gripping the vine with all his might.

Little by little, the friends tugged Ash and Pikachu up the bank of the swamp. Snivy watched the scene from a distance, intrigued to witness such loyalty.

"So Ash?" asked Iris, when he was finally back on solid ground. "Are you still after Snivy now?"

Ash brushed the mud off his clothes and then smiled at her.

"You bet I am!"

Iris couldn't understand how Ash could keep up the pressure. They'd already followed Snivy from one end of the forest to the other, and they were still no closer to capturing it!

"Snivy isn't going to just let you catch it," she blurted out. "Accept the fact that it is not happening!"

"Sorry, but there's no way I'm going to give it up!" promised Ash. "Snivy is as good as mine!"

The Trainer pushed on after the elusive Pokémon, trailing it all the way to a riverbank. Snivy's eyes lit up with recognition when Ash and Pikachu appeared behind it.

"Alright Tepig," shouted Ash. "I choose you!"

Suddenly Tepig appeared from its Poké Ball, energised and ready for action!

"A Fire-type like Tepig does have an advantage over a Grass-type like Snivy," Cilan said hopefully.

"Here's the deal," cried Ash. "You need to attack before Snivy uses Attract!"

Tepig went in with Ember, but yet again Snivy pulled off another slick dodge. Before it knew it, the Grass-type was using Attract all over again! Tepig was completely infatuated.

"Man!" groaned Ash, his fists clenched with frustration. "This won't work! Return!"

Pikachu was preparing to take another turn, when Pidove began to coo loudly and circle above the Trainer's head.

"OK, let's give you a shout!" agreed Ash.

Iris scratched her head. "Why did he stop Pikachu?"

"Because a Flying-type like Pidove has an advantage over a Grass-type like Snivy," explained Cilan.

That was all very well, but if Pidove couldn't deal with Attract this battle would end up the same as all the other ones!

"Use Gust, Pidove!" urged Ash. "Now Quick Attack!"

Pidove's moves were impressive, but true to form Snivy replied with its powerful Attract.

Tension filled the air, as Ash, Iris and Cilan craned their necks to see Pidove's response. The Flying-type froze for an instant, then beat its wings and flew on a new trajectory.

"Pidove wasn't affected at all!" cried Cilan. "It has to be a girl. I bet Ash knew that all along!"

Ash smiled sheepishly – Pidove turning out to be a girl had been one lucky break!

Seeing that Pidove was resistant to Attract, Snivy went back on the offensive.

This time, however Ash was ready for the Pokémon's attacks. The Trainer quickly directed Pidove away from Snivy's Vine Whip and Leaf Storm, responding with Gust, Air Cutter and Quick Attack.

Pidove powered through the skies like a jet plane, noticeably phasing Snivy.

"Oh my!" gasped Iris, taking it all in. For the first time today, it seemed like Ash has a real chance of adding Snivy to the team!

"Snivy!"

The Pokémon tried to fight back against Gust, but it looked weakened and in need of a rest.

Ash saw his moment, pulling out a Poké Ball and hurling it at the Grass-type.

Iris and Cilan held their breath as the Poké Ball absorbed Snivy once again.

Snivy stayed in Ash's Poké Ball for a handful of seconds, before pulling off yet another escape.

The Trainer narrowed his eyes and focused. After all this work, there was no way he was going to leave it at that!

"One more time Pidove!" he shouted. "Use Quick Attack!"

Pidove soared far off into the distance, returning a few moments later at an astonishing speed. Light streamed from its wings as it gathered ever more momentum. The Flying-type blasted Snivy, then circled back round in preparation for its next move.

"Way to go!" cheered Ash. "Now use Air Cutter!"

"It's starting to work!" exclaimed Iris.

Unable to run away, Snivy had now become an easy target. The Pokémon rolled to the ground, its head dropped in submission.

As Snivy began to climb back on its feet, Ash decided that it was now or never.

"Go Poké Ball!" he yelled, throwing it at Snivy one last time.

Iris and Cilan stepped forward for a closer look – would Snivy be willing to accept capture this time around?

A tiny smile glanced across the Pokémon's face before it disappeared into the Poké Ball. The gang gathered round and watched for a few tense moments. The Poké Ball flashed with light and shuddered for what seemed like an eternity before finally going out. Snivy had accepted Ash's capture at last!

"Alright!" clapped Ash, his face filled with pride. "I caught a Snivy! Come on out!"

The Pokémon immediately re-appeared in front of Ash, respectful in defeat. The expression on Snivy's face made it clear that it was thrilled to be caught by such a brave and determined Trainer!

"I'm so glad that you're on board," said Ash with a smile. "Now together, let's you and I win the Unova League!"

The League presented yet another massive challenge, but Ash Ketchum had no doubts at all that he could do it! Now he had five awesome Pokémon on his side, each one loyal, plucky and strong. The Trainer couldn't wait to put them to the test in his next Gym battle. The gang headed back for the trail and the sights of Nacrene City.

Despite their squabbles, even Iris had to agree that the kid had done well this time. She shot a secret smile at Cilan – with Ash around, you never knew what to expect next!

And so Ash again sets his sights on the Gym battle challenge in Nacrene City, now with a remarkable Snivy as his fifth Pokémon in the Unova region.

CHALLENGE CILAN!

Cilan's vast Pokémon knowledge has been gradually built up over years. Now you can pit your wits against the Gym Leader in this mini Pokémon quiz! Study the clues and then use your Trainer experience to identify each of the four species hiding on this page.

1. Steel-type

Composed of two minigears

K L I N K

2. The Desert Croc Pokémon

Stays buried in the sand

S a N D i l e ✓

3. The Multiplying Pokémon

Arms that can crush rock

R E u n i c u s

4. Bug-and-Rock-type

Saliva can melt stone

D w e B B l e

Don't forget to use the Pokédex pages to help you! Turn to page 34.

POKÉMON PATTERNS

A herd of wild Pokémon are lining up to drink from one of Unova's mighty rivers. Could it be that the species are taking turns to quench their thirst? Pore over each orderly queue and then draw in the correct Pokémon to complete the sequence.

1

2

3

4

Don't forget to check your answers on page 77.

I Choose YOU!

Now that Ash has found a great group of Pokémon to follow him, he's ready to take on anything that the Unova region has to offer! The plucky Trainer will keep on battling and exploring until he finally becomes a Pokémon Master. Who knows where his adventures will take him next?

Colour in this picture of Ash and his pals. Can you draw yourself next to the Trainer?

I ❤ you Pokemon

ANSWERS

Page 14. Pikachu Problem
Correct Pikachu is F

Page 15. Ten in Ten?

D	Y	T	I	C	N	O	T	A	I	R	T	S	A	R	W
Y	F	J	K	D	U	N	D	E	L	L	A	B	A	Y	
N	T	S	E	R	O	F	L	E	E	H	W	N	I	P	
W	B	I	C	H	F	H	G	H	E	R	W	U	N	U	
O	P	Z	C	D	S	C	H	I	T	O	C	U	B	K	
T	J	H	T	E	K	M	J	S	T	B	Q	E	O	L	
A	M	K	J	K	N	N	S	A	B	U	K	M	W	S	
I	J	G	N	G	B	E	L	F	H	S	P	A	U	Z	
R	M	Q	A	B	Z	U	R	H	D	C	T	T	A	W	
U	H	C	S	D	M	M	C	C	W	B	S	O	L	A	
H	S	H	Z	U	S	Y	H	G	A	J	H	W	L	F	
U	F	G	C	H	C	T	W	R	B	N	Y	N	E	T	
L	D	C	I	T	F	G	H	I	G	T	T	G	Y	J	
C	A	S	T	E	L	I	A	C	I	T	Y	B	N	L	
K	E	G	U	I	R	D	W	O	R	R	A	Y	K	S	

Page 16. Type Test
1. C, 2. E, 3. B, 4. G, 5. H, 6. F, 7. A, 8. D

Pages 28-29. Changing Faces

Page 30. Zany Zooms
1. IRIS, 2. JAMES, 3. ASH, 4. CILAN, 5. JESSIE
6. PROFESSOR JUNIPER

Page 31. The Road To Striaton City

Pages 44. Liar Liar
3. Team Rocket's boss is known as Giovanni.
6. James originally came from a wealthy family.
7. Team Rocket are just a part of a larger criminal organization.

Page 45. Axew Attack!

Pages 58-59. Pokémon Battle Club!
1. a, 2. c, 3. c, 4. b, 5. a, 6. b, 7. a, 8. c, 9. c, 10. b.

Page 60. Missing Pokémon

Pages 62-63. Coded Carvings
RESHIRAM AND ZEKROM – TWIN HEROES OF UNOVA!

Page 74. Challenge Cilan!
1. KLINK, 2. SANDILE, 3. REUNICLUS, 4. DWEBBLE.

Page 75. Pokémon Patterns
1   2   3   4